Contents

Key point

The **denominator** shows how many equal parts the whole is split into.
The **numerator** shows how many of these parts are being described.

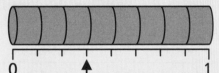

numerator $\longrightarrow$ $\dfrac{3}{8}$ The whole is split into **8 equal parts** and
denominator $\longrightarrow$ the fraction is showing **3 of those parts**.

Wholes can take many forms, including shapes, units of measurement, sets of objects, and numbers on a number line.

Get started

1 Colour $\dfrac{1}{8}$ of this circle.

2 What fraction of this rectangle is red?

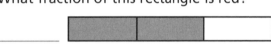

3 What is the denominator of three-quarters?

_____

4 What is the numerator of three-fifths?

_____

5 How many equal parts should this line be split into to show $\dfrac{1}{8}$?

_____

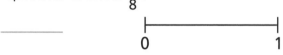

0   1

6 True or false? The denominator of two-thirds is 2.

True ☐   False ☐

7 Colour one of these rectangles to show $\dfrac{2}{5}$.

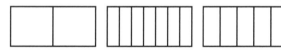

8 A fraction has the denominator 5 and the numerator 4. Write this fraction in words.

_____

Now try these

9 How many equal groups would you sort these flowers into to show $\dfrac{1}{6}$ of the whole set? _____

10 How many groups of flowers would be $\dfrac{5}{6}$ of the whole set? _____

11 What fraction does A stand for on the number line? _____

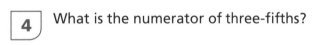

0   1

A

12 Tick the diagram where $\frac{4}{7}$ of the shape is red.

13 How many lots of $\frac{1}{10}$ are equal to $\frac{3}{10}$? _____

14 There are 3 yellow tennis balls and 5 green ones. What fraction of the balls are yellow? _____

15 Jacob wants to colour some parts of this rectangle to show a fraction.
What will the denominator of the fraction be? _____

16 Anna says that three-fifths of this shape is red.
Is she correct?

Yes ☐   No ☐

Challenge

17 The pupils in a class get into equal groups.
What fraction of the pupils in this class is 1 group? _____

18 How many pupils are there in $\frac{2}{7}$ of the class? _____

19 One-third of a 1kg bag of flour is put into a bowl.
What fraction of a kilogram is left in the bag? _____ kg

20 True or false? If the numerator of a fraction is larger than
its denominator, the fraction is greater than one whole.   True ☐   False ☐

21 Abdul says that when the numerator of a fraction is the same as its
denominator, the fraction is equivalent to the number 1. Is he correct?   Yes ☐   No ☐

22 A day has 24 hours. Bobby spent 7 hours asleep.
For what fraction of the day was he asleep? _____

23 Two fractions have the same numerator. Fraction A's
denominator is larger than fraction B's denominator.
Circle the fraction that is larger.

fraction A   fraction B

24 Zainab writes a fraction with the numerator 1.
Her fraction is greater than one-third. What is the denominator of her fraction? _____

Key point

Fractions can stand for areas of shapes, measurements, sets of objects, numbers on a line and so on.

To find fractions of sets of objects, **arrange them into equal groups**.

You can draw **loops** to divide these 18 squares into groups.

 Each **row** is $\frac{1}{3}$.   Each **column** is $\frac{1}{6}$.

$\frac{2}{3}$ of 18 is 2 rows = 12 squares $\frac{5}{6}$ of 18 is 5 columns = 15 squares

Get started

1 Colour four-fifths of these fish.

2 How many squares in $\frac{1}{4}$ of this grid?

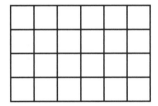

_____

3 Mark $\frac{5}{8}$ on this line with a cross.

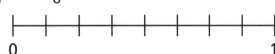

0   1

4 A loaf of bread is cut into seven equal slices. What fraction of the whole loaf is five slices? _____

5 A bag of peppers contains 4 green and 5 red peppers. What fraction of the peppers are green? _____

6 Colour seven-twelfths of this rectangle.

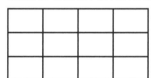

7 Write what fraction of the rectangle above is now not coloured.

_____

8 What fraction of the cubes are red?

_____

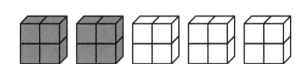

Now try these

9 A packet contains 10 sweets. What fraction of the whole packet is 3 sweets? _____

10 Colour $\frac{2}{3}$ of these caps.

11 What fraction of this rectangle is red?
Write a fraction with the numerator 3. _____

12 Colour four-fifths of this rectangle.

13 How many is $\frac{4}{5}$ of 10 squares? _____

14 How many pencils is five-sixths of a set of 18 pencils? _____

15 For each diagram, write the fraction of marbles that are white.
Give both fractions with the numerator 2.

a) _____

b) _____

16 If A shows one-fifth of a litre,
which letter shows $\frac{3}{5}$ of a litre? _____

Challenge

empty
0

full
1

17 On a battery the red part shows how much power
remains. Estimate what fraction of the power remains. _____

18 A centimetre is split into 10 millimetres. What fraction of a centimetre is 7mm? _____ cm

19 Louise has five 20p coins, making a total of £1. What fraction of one pound is:

a) 20p? _____   b) 60p? _____

20 True or false? Three-quarters of 1 metre is 25cm.   True ☐   False ☐

21 A box contains 4 red crayons, 2 yellow crayons and 5 blue crayons. What fraction of the crayons are:

a) red? _____   b) yellow? _____   c) blue? _____

22 Of 12 mugs on the table, one-third are stripy. How many stripy mugs are there? _____

23 Tick more squares so that three-quarters of the squares
in this grid are ticked.

24 A floor is made from 6 rows of 10 tiles all the same size. One-tenth of the tiles are coloured dark
green and $\frac{1}{6}$ are light green. The rest are white. How many of the tiles are white? _____

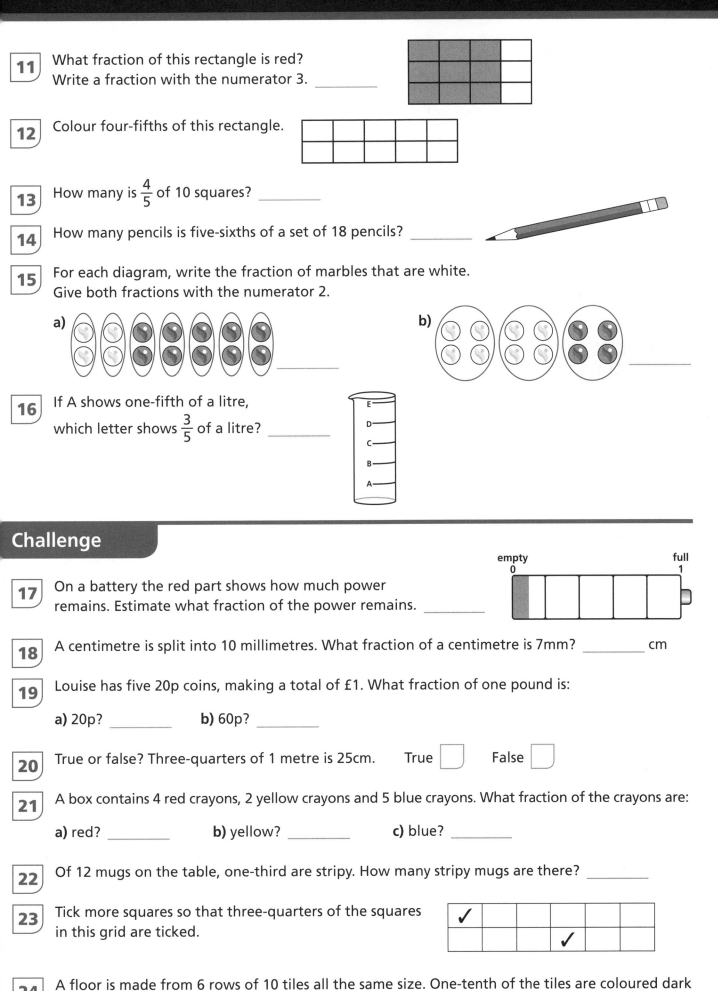

UNIT 3 Recognise mixed numbers

Key point

Mixed numbers are numbers that include a whole number and a fraction, such as $4\frac{1}{2}$ or $5\frac{4}{5}$.

When finding mixed numbers on a number line, look carefully to see how many equal parts each whole number has been split into.

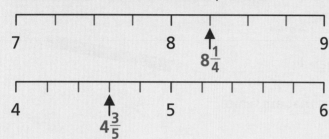

Here each whole is split into **quarters**.

Here each whole is split into **fifths**.

Get started

1 Write the number shown by the arrow.

_____

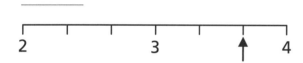

2 Mark $2\frac{1}{3}$ on the line above with a cross.

3 What fraction is each part on this number line? _____

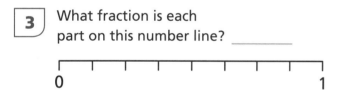

4 What is three-eighths more than 5 wholes? _____

5 Which is larger: $4\frac{3}{5}$ or $5\frac{1}{3}$? _____

6 Write the next two numbers in this sequence.

4, $4\frac{1}{5}$, $4\frac{2}{5}$, $4\frac{3}{5}$, $4\frac{4}{5}$, _____ , _____

7 Mark $\frac{5}{6}$ and $2\frac{3}{6}$ on this number line.

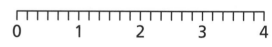

8 Circle the mixed number that lies between the whole numbers 2 and 3.

$1\frac{1}{3}$ $3\frac{1}{2}$ $1\frac{2}{3}$ $2\frac{4}{5}$ $5\frac{2}{3}$ $3\frac{7}{8}$

Now try these

9 When writing the mixed number shown by the arrow, how many times will you write the digit 5? _____

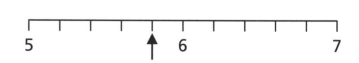

10 When counting on in sixths, which number comes next after $2\frac{5}{6}$? _____

11 What is $\frac{4}{10}$ more than $3\frac{7}{10}$? _____

12 Mark a cross on the ruler to show $2\frac{3}{10}$ cm.

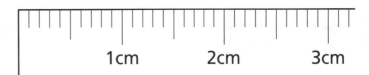

1cm   2cm   3cm

13 How many tenths in:

a) $\frac{7}{10}$? _____   b) 3 wholes? _____   c) $1\frac{5}{10}$? _____

14 Isabel says that the mixed number $2\frac{5}{10}$ is halfway between 2 and 3. Is she correct?

Yes ☐   No ☐

15 Circle the fraction closest to the whole number 7.

$6\frac{1}{4}$ $7\frac{3}{4}$ $6\frac{1}{2}$ $7\frac{1}{2}$ $6\frac{3}{4}$

16 True or false? $2\frac{2}{3}$ is greater than $3\frac{1}{3}$.   True ☐   False ☐

Challenge

17 Write these mixed numbers in order from smallest to largest.

$5\frac{2}{3}$ $1\frac{1}{3}$ $3\frac{1}{2}$ $2\frac{4}{5}$ _____ _____ _____ _____

18 Use the digits 7, 3 and 2 to write the smallest mixed number possible. _____

19 Count on five-sixths from the arrow on the line.
Which number do you land on?   _____   5   6 ↑   7   8   9

20 Jack jumps $4\frac{9}{10}$ m in the long jump. Caitlin jumps $5\frac{6}{10}$ m.

How much further does Caitlin jump than Jack?   _____ m

21 Count back three-eighths from 3. What mixed number do you reach? _____

22 True or false? $1\frac{7}{12} + 7\frac{5}{12} = 9$ True ☐   False ☐

23 What mixed number is 6 less than $10\frac{7}{9}$? _____

24 A builders' merchant sells bags of sand of
different masses as shown here.
Chris buys 3 bags weighing a total of 20kg.
Which 3 bags does she buy? Circle them.

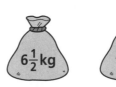
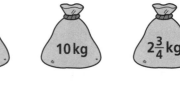

$6\frac{1}{2}$ kg   10 kg $2\frac{3}{4}$ kg

$4\frac{1}{2}$ kg $8\frac{3}{4}$ kg $8\frac{1}{2}$ kg

9

UNIT 4 Find equivalent fractions using a fraction wall

Key point

Fractions that stand for the same amount are **equivalent**.

 $\frac{3}{4}$ is equivalent to $\frac{6}{8}$.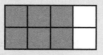

 $\frac{2}{3}$ is equivalent to $\frac{6}{9}$.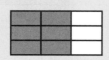

Use a **fraction wall** to find **equivalent fractions** and answer the questions.

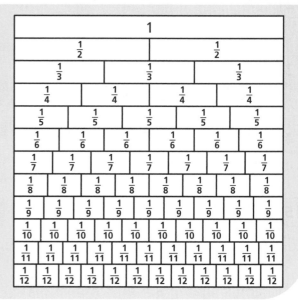

Get started

1 How many sixths are equivalent to $\frac{1}{3}$?

_____ sixths

2 How many tenths are equivalent to one-half?

$\frac{1}{2} = \frac{\boxed{}}{10}$

3 How many eighths are equivalent to one-quarter?

_____ eighths

4 $\frac{3}{4}$ is equivalent to $\frac{\boxed{}}{8}$.

5 How many lots of $\frac{1}{12}$ are equivalent to one whole? _____

6 The fraction $\frac{8}{10}$ is equivalent to how many fifths? _____ fifths

7 $\frac{2}{3} = \frac{\boxed{}}{6}$

8 True or false? $\frac{3}{4} = \frac{9}{12}$

True ☐   False ☐

Now try these

9 What number is missing? $\frac{1}{2}$ is equivalent to $\frac{\boxed{}}{12}$.

10 Fill the gaps with the digits 6 and 2 to create two equivalent fractions. $\frac{1}{\boxed{}} = \frac{3}{\boxed{}}$

11 For each diagram write the fraction of the shape that is red.

a) 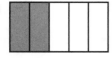 _____

b) 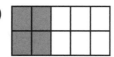 _____

c) 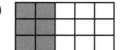 _____

12 A bar of chocolate has 10 chunks. Maddie eats three-fifths of the whole bar. How many chunks does she eat? _____

13 A large pie is cut into 12 equal slices. Jun eats two-thirds of the pie. How many slices does he eat? _____

14 True or false? $\frac{2}{10} = \frac{4}{5}$

True ☐   False ☐

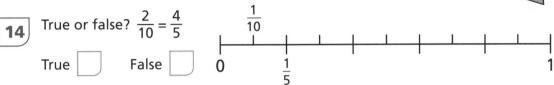

15 Ten out of twelve flowers in a bunch are yellow.
Alice says that five-sixths of the flowers are yellow. Is she correct?   Yes ☐   No ☐

16 Find out if $\frac{4}{9}$ is greater than, less than or equivalent to $\frac{1}{3}$ by using a fraction wall.

_____

Challenge

17 Harry has 9 cupcakes. $\frac{1}{3}$ are chocolate and $\frac{3}{9}$ are vanilla. Does he have more, fewer or the same number of chocolate cupcakes as vanilla cupcakes? _____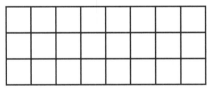

18 In a sports team $\frac{8}{12}$ are girls. How many thirds of the team are girls? _____ thirds

19 A wall is covered in tiles. $\frac{2}{6}$ of the tiles are black. $\frac{4}{12}$ of the tiles are white.

Are there the same number of black tiles as white tiles?   Yes ☐   No ☐

20 True or false? These three fractions are all equivalent: $\frac{3}{4}$ $\frac{6}{8}$ $\frac{8}{12}$ True ☐   False ☐

21 This grid has 24 squares. Joel colours 18 squares.

He then says that $\frac{3}{4}$ is equivalent to $\frac{18}{24}$. Is he correct?

Yes ☐   No ☐

22 Is it possible to fill the gaps of this statement with odd numbers so that it is true?

$\frac{?}{12}$ is equivalent to $\frac{?}{3}$.   Yes ☐   No ☐

23 Iqra has found out that you can multiply the numerator and denominator of a fraction by the same number to get an equivalent fraction.

Multiply the numerator and denominator of $\frac{3}{4}$ by 5 to get an equivalent fraction. _____

24 Write the equivalent fraction produced by multiplying the numerator and denominator of $\frac{2}{3}$ by 8. _____

11

Key point

Fractions with the same value are **equivalent**. This **family** of fractions is equivalent to one-half ($\frac{1}{2}$).

$$\frac{2}{4} \qquad \frac{3}{6} \qquad \frac{4}{8} \qquad \frac{5}{10}$$

If you multiply or divide the numerator and denominator of a fraction **by the same number** you will get an equivalent fraction.

$$\xrightarrow{\div 2} \qquad \xrightarrow{\times 3} \qquad \xrightarrow{\times 4} \qquad \xrightarrow{\div 5}$$

$$\frac{2}{4} \rightarrow \frac{1}{2} \qquad \frac{1}{2} \rightarrow \frac{3}{6} \qquad \frac{1}{2} \rightarrow \frac{4}{8} \qquad \frac{5}{10} \rightarrow \frac{1}{2}$$

$$\xleftarrow{\div 2} \qquad \xleftarrow{\times 3} \qquad \xleftarrow{\times 4} \qquad \xleftarrow{\div 5}$$

Get started

1 What is the missing equivalent fraction? $\frac{3}{4}$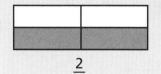

2 Find the equivalent fraction. $\frac{3}{4}$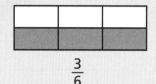

3 What is missing? $\frac{9}{12}$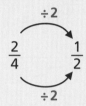

4 What number has the numerator and denominator of two-fifths been multiplied by to give the equivalent fraction four-tenths? $\frac{2}{5}$ 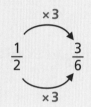 $\frac{4}{10}$

5 The numerator and denominator of $\frac{2}{3}$ are multiplied by 4 to give what equivalent fraction? _____

6 The numerator and denominator of $\frac{5}{15}$ are divided by 5 to give what equivalent fraction? _____

7 Multiply both numbers of the fraction $\frac{5}{6}$ by 2 to give an equivalent fraction.

_____

8 What number have both numbers of the first fraction been divided by to give the equivalent fraction? $\frac{21}{30}$ 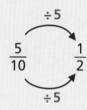 $\frac{7}{10}$

Now try these

9 True or false? $\frac{3}{5} = \frac{9}{15}$

True ☐　　　False ☐

10 What is the missing number? $\frac{2}{3}$ is equivalent to $\dfrac{\boxed{}}{9}$.

11 True or false? These fractions are all equivalent: $\frac{2}{8} = \frac{1}{4} = \frac{3}{12}$ True ☐   False ☐

12 Circle the fraction that is equivalent to $\frac{2}{5}$.

$\frac{1}{10}$ $\frac{2}{10}$ $\frac{3}{10}$ $\frac{4}{10}$ $\frac{5}{10}$

13 Complete the equivalent fractions. $\frac{1}{2} = \frac{\Box}{10} = \frac{\Box}{12}$

14 Matthew says that $\frac{2}{3}$ is equivalent to $\frac{200}{300}$. Is he correct?   Yes ☐   No ☐

15 Is $\frac{30}{40}$ equivalent to $\frac{9}{12}$? $\frac{30}{40}$ $\overset{÷\,?}{\underset{÷\,?}{\frown}}$ $\frac{3}{4}$ $\overset{×\,?}{\underset{×\,?}{\frown}}$ $\frac{9}{12}$ Yes ☐   No ☐

16 Natasha says that $\frac{2}{4}$ is not equivalent to $\frac{3}{6}$. Is she correct?   Yes ☐   No ☐

Challenge

17 15 of these 18 stars are red. The stars are grouped into sixths.

How many sixths are red? $\frac{15}{18} = \frac{\Box}{6}$

18 Write a fraction equivalent to $\frac{1}{3}$ with the denominator 15. _____

19 The 12 buttons below have been grouped in different ways.
Write three equivalent fractions to show what fraction of them are white.

a)   b)   c)

_____   _____   _____

20 Complete this pattern. $\frac{1}{3} = \frac{\Box}{6} = \frac{\Box}{12}$

21 Circle the fraction that is not equivalent to the others. $\frac{1}{5}$ $\frac{2}{10}$ $\frac{3}{15}$ $\frac{4}{20}$ $\frac{5}{30}$

22 Ffion notices that $\frac{3}{8}$ of some counters are blue.
If there are 9 blue counters, how many counters are there in total? _____

23 There are 32 people on a bus. If $\frac{3}{8}$ of the people
are male, how many people on the bus are male? _____

24 A grid of 24 squares has 16 coloured green. What proportion
of the squares are green? Give your answer as a fraction with the numerator 2. _____

Key point

When adding or subtracting fractions, if the denominators are the same, **add or subtract the numerators only**.
The denominator stays the same.

numerator $\longrightarrow$
denominator $\longrightarrow$ $\dfrac{3}{10} + \dfrac{6}{10} = \dfrac{9}{10}$ $\dfrac{9}{10} - \dfrac{6}{10} = \dfrac{3}{10}$

Some answers may be greater than 1. These answers can be given as an **improper fraction** (top-heavy fraction) or as a **mixed number** (a whole number and a fraction).

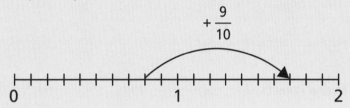

$+\dfrac{9}{10}$

improper   mixed
fraction   number

$\dfrac{8}{10} + \dfrac{9}{10} = \dfrac{17}{10} = 1\dfrac{7}{10}$

Get started

1 $\dfrac{2}{9} + \dfrac{3}{9} = \dfrac{5}{}$

2 $\dfrac{7}{10} + \dfrac{6}{10} = \dfrac{13}{}$

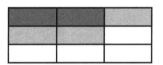

3 $\dfrac{6}{7} - \dfrac{3}{7} = \dfrac{}{7}$

4 $\dfrac{8}{10} - \dfrac{3}{10} = \dfrac{}{}$

5 $\dfrac{2}{4} + \dfrac{3}{4} = \dfrac{}{}$

6 $\dfrac{}{9} + \dfrac{3}{9} = \dfrac{10}{9}$

7 $\dfrac{11}{12} - \dfrac{}{} = \dfrac{4}{12}$

8 $\dfrac{3}{8} + \dfrac{1}{8} + \dfrac{3}{8} = \dfrac{}{}$

Now try these

9 Add $\dfrac{2}{5}$ to $\dfrac{4}{5}$. Give your answer as a mixed number. _____

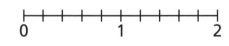

10 Subtract $\dfrac{3}{8}$ from $\dfrac{7}{8}$. Give your answer as an equivalent fraction with the numerator 1. _____

11 How many sevenths is the answer to five-sevenths plus four-sevenths? _____ sevenths

12 Find the values of a and b. $\dfrac{8}{10} - \dfrac{3}{10} = \dfrac{a}{10} = \dfrac{1}{b}$ $a =$ _____ $b =$ _____

13 Give the sum of five-sixths and two-sixths as a mixed number. _____

14 Give the sum of four-ninths, five-ninths and four-ninths as an improper fraction. _____

15 Decrease $\frac{7}{8}$ by $\frac{2}{8}$. _____

16

$\frac{7}{12}$	$\frac{5}{12}$	$\frac{9}{12}$	$\frac{4}{12}$	$\frac{11}{12}$

Look at the fractions above. What is the largest fraction minus the smallest fraction? _____

Challenge

17 In a litter of puppies, $\frac{1}{5}$ are black, $\frac{2}{5}$ are golden and the
rest are brown. What fraction of the puppies are brown? _____

18 Write the answer to $\frac{6}{5} + \frac{4}{5} - \frac{2}{5}$ as an improper fraction and as a mixed number.

_____ and _____

19 A bag of flour weighs $\frac{9}{10}$kg. Ben uses $\frac{7}{10}$kg of the flour to make a batter.

   a) What fraction of a kilogram is left? _____ kg

   b) How many grams is this? _____ g

20 When $\frac{8}{10}$m is added to $\frac{6}{10}$m, what fraction
of a metre more than 1 whole metre is the result? _____ m

21 Adam and Ruben buy two pizzas. Each eats $\frac{5}{8}$ of a pizza. If each pizza
is cut equally into eight slices, what is the total number of slices not eaten? _____

22 $\boxed{\frac{5}{15} = \frac{1}{3}}$ Use this fact to help you find the difference between $\frac{12}{15}$ and $\frac{1}{3}$. _____

23 $\boxed{\frac{21}{24} = \frac{7}{8}}$ Use this fact to help you find the sum of $\frac{7}{8}$ and $\frac{15}{24}$.

Give your answer as a mixed number. _____

24 Poppy spent $\frac{7}{12}$ of an hour watching a cartoon
and $\frac{6}{12}$ of an hour watching a quiz show.

   a) Write the total fraction of time she spent watching these, as a mixed number. _____ hr

   b) How many minutes is this? _____ min

1 Write the fraction of this rectangle that is red.

_____

1 mark

2 Oscar has 4 yellow t-shirts and 3 green ones in his wardrobe.
What fraction of Oscar's t-shirts are yellow?

_____

1 mark

3 True or false? If the denominator of a fraction is larger
than its numerator the fraction is greater than 1 whole.

True ☐   False ☐

1 mark

4 How many squares in $\frac{3}{4}$ of this grid? _____

1 mark

5 Colour $\frac{2}{3}$ of these snails.

1 mark

6 A centimetre is split into 10 millimetres.
What fraction of a centimetre is 3mm? _____ cm

1 mark

7 Mark $\frac{4}{6}$ and $3\frac{1}{6}$ on this line.

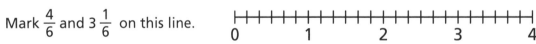

1 mark

8 What is $\frac{7}{10}$ more than $2\frac{9}{10}$?

_____

1 mark

9 Circle the fraction closest to the whole number 6.

$5\frac{1}{2}$ $5\frac{3}{4}$ $6\frac{1}{2}$ $7\frac{1}{2}$ $6\frac{3}{4}$

1 mark

10 Count back five-sixths from 2.
What mixed number do you reach? _____

1 mark

11 How many lots of $\frac{1}{9}$ are equivalent to one whole? _____

☐
1 mark

12 For each diagram, write the fraction of the shape that is red.

a)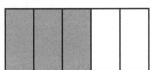

b)

c)

_____   _____   _____

☐
1 mark

13 12 out of 15 pens in a pencil case are blue.

John says that three-fifths of the pens are blue. Is he correct?

Yes ☐   No ☐

☐
1 mark

14 In a football team $\frac{9}{12}$ are girls.

How many quarters of the team are girls? _____ quarters

☐
1 mark

15 Write the equivalent fraction produced

by multiplying the numerator and denominator of $\frac{4}{5}$ by 6. _____

☐
1 mark

16 True or false? $\frac{3}{4} = \frac{9}{12}$

True ☐   False ☐

☐
1 mark

17 Write a fraction equivalent to $\frac{1}{4}$ with the denominator 12. _____

☐
1 mark

18 $\frac{8}{10} - \frac{5}{10} = \boxed{}$

☐
1 mark

19 Subtract $\frac{5}{12}$ from $\frac{11}{12}$.

Give your answer as an equivalent fraction with the numerator 1. _____

☐
1 mark

20 $\frac{3}{10}$ m is added to $\frac{9}{10}$ m.

What fraction of a metre more than one whole metre is the result? _____ m

☐
1 mark

Total

☐
20 marks

17

Key point

Tenths can be shown as fractions and decimals. The column to the right of the **decimal point** is the tenths column.

tenths	fraction or mixed number	decimal ones . tenths
	$\frac{1}{10}$	0 . 1
	$\frac{2}{10}$	0 . 2
	$\frac{5}{10}$	0 . 5
	$1\frac{4}{10}$	1 . 4

Get started

1 Write as a decimal how much of this rectangle is red.

_____

2 Write 0.7 as a fraction. _____

3 How many tenths are there in 0.5?
_____ tenths

4 What is the missing number?

[ ] tenths = $\frac{9}{10}$

5 Write eight-tenths as a decimal and as a fraction.

_____ and _____

6 How many tenths more is 0.8 than $\frac{6}{10}$?

_____ tenths

7 Write what the arrow is pointing to as a decimal. _____

8 Colour 0.5 of this circle.

Now try these

9 A chocolate bar has 10 equal chunks.
Write as a decimal how much of the bar is six chunks. _____

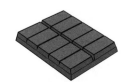

10 True or false? 0.5 is equivalent to $\frac{1}{2}$.   True ☐   False ☐

11 True or false? 1.2 is equivalent to the mixed number $1\frac{2}{10}$.   True ☐   False ☐

12 Write $2\frac{7}{10}$ as a decimal. _____

13 True or false? 2.9kg is one-tenth of a kilogram less than 3 whole kilograms.   True ☐   False ☐

14 Write the missing numbers.   5.3 = ☐ ones + ☐ tenths

15 Continue the sequence.   0.6, 0.7, 0.8, 0.9, _____ , _____

16 Mark 2.4cm on this ruler.

1cm   2cm   3cm

Challenge

17 Write the missing numbers.   17.6 = ☐ ten + ☐ ones + ☐ tenths

18 A line of 10 square tiles measures 9m.

a) How long is each tile, as a fraction of a metre? _____ m

b) What is this length as a decimal? _____ m

19 Ten identical books weigh 8kg in total.
What does one book weigh, written as a decimal? _____ kg

20 What fraction of this shape   is this shape?

Write your answer as a fraction and as a decimal. _____ and _____

21 6.5 litres can be written as $6\frac{5}{10}$ litres or $6\frac{1}{?}$ litres. What is the missing number? _____

22 A bag of sugar is 2kg. Each jar holds 0.2kg of sugar.
How many jars are needed for all the sugar? _____

23 A class of 30 pupils get into 10 equal groups with 3 children in each group.
What proportion of the class are 6 of the children? Write your answer as a decimal. _____

24 In a bunch of 20 flowers, 4 are blue, 10 are white and the rest are red. As a decimal, what proportion of all the flowers are red? _____

Key point

Tenths **less than** one whole can be written as fractions or as decimals.

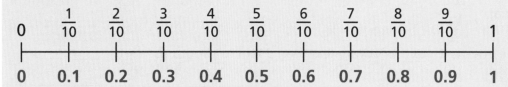

Tenths **greater than** one whole can be written as mixed numbers, improper fractions or decimals.

The arrow points to $1\frac{7}{10}$ or 1.7.

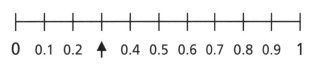

Get started

1 What decimal is marked with an arrow? _____

```
├──┼──┼──┼──┼──┼──┼──┼──┼──┼──┤
0  0.1 0.2  ↑  0.4 0.5 0.6 0.7 0.8 0.9  1
```

2 Continue the sequence.

1.7, 1.8, 1.9, 2, _____ , _____

3 What is one-tenth more than $\frac{8}{10}$ as a decimal? _____

4 What decimal is two-tenths less than one whole? _____

5 How many tenths of a metre make 1 whole metre?

_____ tenths

6 Write the next number in the sequence, as a fraction and as a decimal.

$3\frac{6}{10}$, $3\frac{7}{10}$, $3\frac{8}{10}$, _____ or _____

7 Mark 0.5 and 1.4 on this line.

```
├┼┼┼┼┼┼┼┼┼┼┼┼┼┼┼┼┼┼┼┼┤
0           1           2
```

8 How many tenths of a metre make:

a) $\frac{1}{2}$ a metre? _____ tenths

b) two whole metres? _____ tenths

Now try these

9 Which decimal (with one digit after the decimal point) lies between 2.6 and 2.8? _____

10 What digit is missing to give the mass shown? | 8. | kg

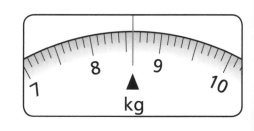

11 Write these decimals in order from smallest to largest.

5.1   5.3   5.2   5.4   _____   _____   _____   _____

12 Write the mixed number $4\frac{1}{10}$ as a decimal. _____

13 True or false? 1.2 is two-tenths larger than 0.9.

True ☐   False ☐

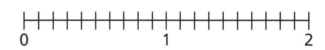

14 True or false? 14 tenths is the same as 1.4.

True ☐   False ☐

15 Write the mixed number $2\frac{1}{2}$ as a decimal. _____

16 Count back six-tenths from 2. What decimal do you reach? _____

Challenge

17 A millimetre is one-tenth of a centimetre. How many millimetres is 0.6cm? _____ mm

18 How many millimetres is 1.9cm? _____ mm

19 Mark the decimals 0.7, 1.7 and 2.7 on the line.

20 How many tenths is the difference between one whole and 0.6? _____ tenths

21 Some square tiles have sides that are each one-tenth of a metre.
How long is a line of 13 touching tiles, in metres?
Give your answer as a decimal. _____ m

22 Write the missing decimals in this sequence.

1.5, _____ , 1.3, 1.2, _____ , 1

23 A tap drips 0.1 litre of water every minute.
How many litres will it drip in 30 minutes? _____ l

24 Jade ran a race in 10.5 seconds.
Isla took seven-tenths of a second longer.

How long did Isla take?

_____ sec

UNIT 9 Order and round decimals with one decimal place

Key point

The **blue** line is **0.9cm** long.
The nearest whole centimetre to 0.9cm is 1cm.
0.9 rounded to the nearest whole number is **1**.

The **red** line is **2.3cm** long.
The nearest whole centimetre to 2.3cm is 2cm.
2.3 rounded to the nearest whole number is **2**.

1cm   2cm

If a number is **halfway** between two whole numbers (when the tenths digit is 5), **round up**.
3.5 rounds up to 4.

2.3 > 0.9 means 2.3 is **greater than** 0.9.

Get started

1 Mark 0.7 on this number line.

0   1

2 Is 0.7 nearer to 0 or 1? _____

3 Circle which is greater.   0.7   0.2

4 Which whole number is
3.8 closest to: 3 or 4? _____

5 Which is greater: 1.4 or 4.1? _____

6 Circle the shorter length.   2.9cm   3.1cm

7 Is 4.5kg more or less than 5kg?

_____

8 Round 1.6 to the
nearest whole number. _____

Now try these

9 True or false? 1.0 is smaller than 0.9.   True ☐   False ☐

10 Use the < or > sign to show which is larger.   2.4 ☐ 4.2

11 If you like chocolate, would you prefer to be given 2.3 bars or 1.8 bars?

_____

12 What is 6.5kg rounded to the nearest whole kilogram? _____ kg

13 Round 10.3 to the nearest whole number. _____

14 True or false?   9.9 < 10   True ☐   False ☐

15 Write the length of the line to the nearest centimetre.

_____ cm

16 Put these decimals in order from smallest to largest.

2.4   3.1   1.9   _____   _____   _____

Challenge

17 David is 0.8m tall. His brother is 1.1m tall. Is David taller or shorter than his brother?

_____

18 Some athletes are doing the long jump.
Their distances jumped are shown:

Seb 4.1m   Max 2.8m   Joel 3.2m   Ali 3.8m

Which two athletes' jumps are 4 metres
when rounded to the nearest whole metre?

_____ and _____

19 Put the above jumps in order from smallest to largest.

_____ m   _____ m   _____ m   _____ m

20 Circle all the decimals that round to 6 when rounded to the nearest whole number.

4.9   3.6   6.7   5.5   4.6   6.4   6.1   0.6

21 14 tenths is the same as 1 whole and 4 tenths. How is 14 tenths written as a decimal?

_____

22 What is the smallest decimal with one decimal place (one digit after the
decimal point) that is 3 when rounded to the nearest whole number?

_____

23 Hafsa throws a beanbag 4.3m. Milly throws another
beanbag 5.3m. How much further does Milly's beanbag travel? _____ m

24 A camera takes a photo every tenth of a second.
How many photos are taken in 1.3 seconds?

_____

23

Key point

When **one** pie is shared equally between **10** people each person gets **one-tenth**.
When **two** pies are shared equally between **10** people each person gets **two-tenths**, and so on.

$1 \div 10 = \frac{1}{10} = 0.1$

$2 \div 10 = \frac{2}{10} = 0.2$

If you are giving answers as decimals, you can use **place value** when dividing by **10**. Just move the digits of the number **one place to the right**.

ones	.	tenths
7	.	

$\div 10$

0	.	7

$=$ zero point seven

Get started

1 $4 \div 10 =$ 0.⬜

2 $7 \div 10 =$ ⬜⬜ $= 0.7$

3   What is nine divided by ten, as a decimal? _____

4   ⬜ $\div 10 = 0.3$

5   What is 2 tubs of ice cream shared between 10, as a decimal?

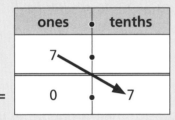

_____

6   What number when divided by 10 gives 0.6? _____

7   What decimal is the arrow pointing to? _____

0   ↑   1

8   Four divided by ten. Write the answer in words as a decimal.

_____

Now try these

9   One pot of yoghurt is shared equally into ten bowls.
Write as a decimal in words how much of the pot is in each bowl. _____

10   Nine pizzas are divided equally between ten people.

    a) What fraction of a pizza does each person get? _____

    b) What is this fraction as a decimal? _____

11 A farmer divides five kilograms of compost equally into 10 bags.

    a) Write as a decimal how much compost is in each bag. _____ kg

    b) Write this as a fraction of a kilogram with the numerator 1. _____ kg

12 A machine makes ten nails from a piece of metal weighing 7g.
What is the weight of each nail as a decimal if no metal is wasted? _____ g

13 An 8m rope is cut into 10 equal lengths.
Write what proportion of a metre each length is as a decimal. _____ m

14 Tick the longest measurement.

    7cm ÷ 10 ☐ $\frac{4}{10}$ cm ☐   0.6cm ☐

15 Three litres of lemonade is poured equally into ten cups.
How much is in each cup? Give your answer as a decimal. _____ l

16 Ten poles are laid touching in a line. Each is 0.6m long.
What is the length of the line? _____ m

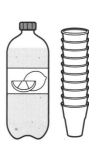

Challenge

17 As she walks, each of Nina's steps is 0.7m apart.
If she takes 10 steps, how far from the start has she walked? _____ m

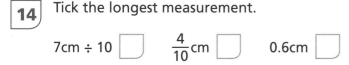

0.7m

18 Ten buckets weigh 9kg in total. As a decimal what does one bucket weigh? _____ kg

19 True or false? 10 lots of 0.4 is 4 wholes.   True ☐   False ☐

20 A line of 10 square tiles measures 5m. How long is each tile, as a decimal? _____ m

21 Divide five by ten. Circle three correct answers. $\frac{1}{5}$ 0.2 0.10 $\frac{5}{10}$ 0.5 $\frac{1}{10}$ 0.1 $\frac{1}{2}$

22 $\boxed{2 \div 10 = \frac{2}{10} = \frac{1}{5}}$

    Look at this fact. Use the fact to write $\frac{1}{5}$ as a decimal. _____

23 Nathan walks from home to work and back again
each day for 5 days. He walks 8km in total.
What is the distance from his home to his work, as a decimal? _____ km

24 Daisy divides a number by 10 and then divides the answer by 10.
If her starting number was 60, what is her final answer? _____

UNIT 11 Divide one- or two-digit numbers by 10

Key point

Any whole number can be easily divided by **10** using **place value** to give a decimal answer. Just move the digits of the number **one place to the right**.

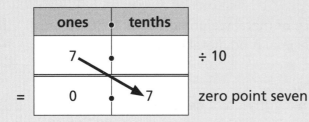

ones	tenths	
7		÷ 10

ones	tenths	
0	7	zero point seven

=

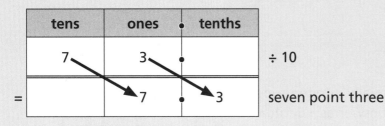

tens	ones	tenths	
7	3		÷ 10

tens	ones	tenths	
	7	3	seven point three

=

Get started

1 Divide the number in the grid by 10.

O	t
8	

_____

2 Divide the number in the grid by 10.

T	O	t
8	3	

_____

3 $7 \div 10 =$ | 0. |

4 Write the answer to $13 \div 10$ as a decimal.

_____

5 What is nineteen divided by ten, as a decimal? _____

6 [ ] $\div 10 = 3.5$

7 What is 12 cakes shared equally between 10, as a decimal?

_____

8 What number when divided by 10 gives 2.7? _____

Now try these

9 The arrow is pointing to the answer to this question: [ ] $\div 10$
What is the missing number in the question?

10 A class is arranged into 10 teams. The teacher gives each team a 2.5m length of ribbon. What is the total length of all the ribbon? _____ m

11 Mark on the line the answer to 14 divided by 10.

0   1   2   3

12 Divide 8 by 10. Colour parts of this whole rectangle to show the answer.

13 Divide 17 by 10. Colour parts of these whole rectangles to show the answer.

14 If 69 ÷ 10 = 6.9, what is 6.9 × 10? _____

15 What is one-tenth of £95? £_____

16 True or false? 10 lots of 1.3 is 13 wholes.   True ☐   False ☐

Challenge

17 George says seventy divided by 10 is 7. Lauren says seventy divided by 10 is 7.0.

Who is correct? George, Lauren or both? _____

18 A 52cm line is split into 10 equal parts. What is the length of each part:

a) in centimetres? _____ cm   **b)** in millimetres? _____ mm

19 True or false? 25m ÷ 10 = $2\frac{1}{2}$ m   True ☐   False ☐

20 A hose lets out 3.3 litres of water every minute. Joss wants to fill her 33-litre paddling pool. How many minutes will it take to fill it? _____ min

21 Hassan chooses a number to divide by ten. His answer as a mixed number is $7\frac{5}{10}$.

a) What is his answer as a decimal? _____   **b)** What was his chosen number? _____

22 Elena walks slowly in tiny steps across the playground, taking 78 seconds. She then runs back as fast as she can, taking one-tenth of the time. How many seconds does it take her to run back? _____ sec

23 What is one-tenth of 52 plus 52? _____

24 Holly has £6. She spends one-tenth of this money on a cake. How much does she have left afterwards? £_____

Key point

When a number is divided by another, the answer can be written as a fraction.

3 cakes are shared equally between 8 people. Each cake can be split into eighths.

Each person can have $\frac{1}{8}$ of each cake, so each person has $\frac{3}{8}$ altogether.

$3 \div 8 = \frac{3}{8}$ **Notice the numerator and denominator.**

$4 \div 5 = \frac{4}{5}$

The number being divided becomes the numerator and the number being divided by becomes the denominator.

If dividing by 10, the answer can also be written as a decimal. $3 \div 10 = \frac{3}{10} = 0.3$

Get started

1 These three cakes are shared equally between four children.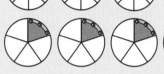
How much does each child get? _____

2 Write the answer to 1 ÷ 2 as a fraction. _____

3 Divide 3 by 7 and give your answer as a fraction. _____

4 $4 \div 5 = \dfrac{4}{\boxed{}}$

5 A whole number is divided by 6 to give the answer $\frac{5}{6}$.
What is the whole number? _____

6 True or false? $7 \div 10 = \frac{7}{10} = 0.7$
True ☐   False ☐

7 Write the answer to 8 divided by 10 as a decimal. _____

8 A whole number divided by 10 gives the answer 0.4.
What is the whole number? _____

Now try these

9 Five doughnuts are equally shared between eight people.
What fraction of a doughnut does each person get? _____

10 Two litres of juice is poured equally into nine empty cups.
What fraction of a litre is in each cup? _____ l

11 Mark the answer to 7 ÷ 8 on this line.

0 ├──┼──┼──┼──┼──┼──┼──┤ 1

12 Give the answer to 9 ÷ 10 as a fraction and as a decimal. _____ and _____

13 Six TV adverts are all the same length of time. If they take 5 minutes in total to show on TV, what fraction of a minute is each advert? _____ min

14 A 2m roll of ribbon is cut into 10 equal lengths. Write, as a decimal, the length of each. _____ m

15 True or false? 5 ÷ 10 and 1 ÷ 2 have the same answer when written as a decimal.

True ☐   False ☐

16 Fill in the missing numbers. $6 \div 8 = \dfrac{}{} = \dfrac{}{4}$

Challenge

17 Peter says that £6 divided by 10 is £0.60. Is he correct?

Yes ☐   No ☐

18 Four identical display boards in a school hall are equally shared between eight classes. Write two equivalent fractions to show what fraction of a board each class has.

_____ and _____

19 Thomas spends one-tenth of £7 on sweets.

a) What fraction of a pound does he spend? _____

b) What is this as a decimal? _____

20 A jug holds 2 litres of water. The water is poured into 10 cups.

a) What fraction of a litre of water does each cup hold? _____ l

b) What is this as a decimal? _____ l

21 What fraction of a metre is each part when a 3m plank is sawn into 10 equal parts?

Give your answer as a fraction and as a decimal. _____ m and _____ m

22 7m ÷ 10 equals how many centimetres? _____ cm

23 If 3 pies shared between 7 equals $\dfrac{3}{7}$, what do 10 pies shared between 7 equal? _____

24 What is 17 divided by 10 as a mixed number and as a decimal? _____ and _____

Check-up test 2

1 How much of this rectangle is red?
Write your answer as a decimal. _____

1 mark

2 A chocolate bar has 10 equal chunks.
Write, as a decimal, how much of the bar is 5 chunks. _____

1 mark

3 A bag of sand weighs 3kg.
Each tub holds 0.3kg of sand.
How many tubs are needed for all the sand? _____   **3 kg**

1 mark

4 What decimal is three-tenths less than one whole? _____

1 mark

5 Which decimal (with one digit after the decimal point)
lies between 3.2 and 3.4? _____

1 mark

6 How many millimetres is 2.4cm?
_____ mm

1 mark

7 Alfie swam a race in 12.7 seconds.
Emily took six-tenths of a second longer.
How long did Emily take? _____ sec

1 mark

8 Mark 0.3 on this number line.

0   1

1 mark

9 Circle the longer length.

1.8cm   2.1cm

1 mark

10 Put these decimals in order from smallest to largest.

2.7   3.4   2.9   _____ _____ _____

1 mark

11 [   ] ÷ 10 = 0.6

1 mark

12 Seven melons are divided between ten people.

a) What fraction of a melon does each person get? _____

b) What is this fraction as a decimal? _____

1 mark

13 Ten boxes are placed touching in a line. Each box is 0.9m long.
What is the length of the line of boxes? _____ m

1 mark

30

14 Niamh cycles from home to work and back again each day for 5 days.
She cycles 9km in total.
What is the distance from her home to her work, as a decimal? _____ km

☐
1 mark

15 Divide the number in the grid by 10.

T	O	•	t
6	4	•	

_____

☐
1 mark

16 Jamie chooses a number to divide by ten. His answer as a mixed number is $5\frac{3}{10}$.

a) What is his answer as a decimal? _____

b) What was his chosen number? _____

☐
1 mark

17 Divide 4 by 9 and give your answer as a fraction.

_____

☐
1 mark

18 A whole number divided by 10 gives the answer 0.7.
What is the whole number?

_____

☐
1 mark

19 What fraction of a metre is each part when a 4m plank
is sawn into 10 equal parts? Give your answer as a
fraction and as a decimal.

_____ m and _____ m

☐
1 mark

20 3m ÷ 10 equals how many centimetres?

_____ cm

☐
1 mark

Total

☐

20 marks

31

Key point

Hundredths can be shown as fractions and decimals. The column to the right of the tenths column is the hundredths column. 10 hundredths is the same as 1 tenth.

		fraction	decimal ones . tenths hundredths
	1 tenth	$\frac{1}{10}$	0 . 1
	1 hundredth	$\frac{1}{100}$	0 . 0 1
	14 hundredths	$\frac{14}{100}$	0 . 1 4
	25 hundredths	$\frac{25}{100}$ or $\frac{1}{4}$	0 . 2 5

Get started

1 How much of this whole is red? Write your answer as a decimal.

_____

2 How many tenths are there in 0.3?

_____ tenths

3 How much of this whole is red? Write your answer as a decimal.

_____

4 Write the decimal 0.01 as a fraction.

_____

5 How many hundredths are there in 0.07?

_____ hundredths

6 Write nine-hundredths as a decimal and as a fraction.

_____ and _____

7 How many hundredths more is 0.08 than $\frac{6}{100}$?

_____ hundredths

8 Write the next two decimals in this sequence.

0.01, 0.02, 0.03, 0.04, _____ , _____

Now try these

9 A toy car is $\frac{7}{100}$ m long. Write this length as a decimal.

_____ m

10 True or false? Ten-hundredths are the same as one-tenth.

True ☐   False ☐

11 If 14 hundredths written as a decimal is 0.14,
how could you write 10 hundredths as a decimal? _____

12 What is the missing number? ☐ hundredths = $\frac{13}{100}$

13 Tick how many hundredths of this shape are red.

34 hundredths ☐   47 hundredths ☐   43 hundredths ☐

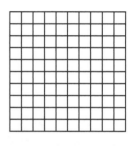

14 $\frac{1}{4}$ of this square is red. $\frac{3}{4}$ of this square is white.
Write $\frac{1}{4}$ and $\frac{3}{4}$ as decimals. _____ and _____

15 Colour 61 hundredths of this whole.

16 If 9 more hundredths of this whole are coloured,
how many tenths would now be coloured altogether? _____ tenths

Challenge

17 Rose says that $\frac{1}{10}$ m is equivalent to $\frac{10}{100}$ m. Is she correct?   Yes ☐   No ☐

18 How many tenths is the same as 30 hundredths? _____ tenths

19 What decimal has no ones, one-tenth and seven-hundredths? _____

20 True or false? $\frac{64}{100}$ = 64 hundredths = 6 tenths + 4 hundredths = 0.64   True ☐   False ☐

21 a) What fraction of a whole metre is a centimetre? _____ m

b) What is this fraction as a decimal? _____ m

22 A bag of rice is 1kg. A scoop can hold 0.01kg of rice.
How many full scoops of rice are in the whole bag?

_____

23 In a school there are exactly 100 pupils. 43 of the children are girls.
As a decimal, what proportion of all the children are: a) girls? _____   b) boys? _____

24 Convert the fractions below to decimals and put them in order from smallest to largest.

$\frac{27}{100}$ $\frac{1}{2}$ $\frac{1}{100}$ $\frac{1}{4}$ _____ _____ _____ _____

Key point

A whole split into tenths is shown on a number line with each tenth written as a fraction or a decimal. Each tenth can be split into 10 equal parts, or 10 **hundredths**.

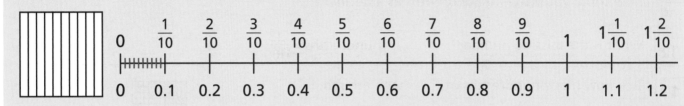

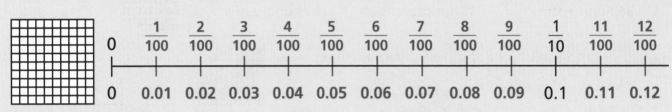

Remember:

ones	•	tenths	hundredths		ones	•	tenths	hundredths
0	•	1	0	=	0	•	1	

Get started

1 What decimal is marked with an arrow? _____

0   0.01 0.02   0.04 0.05 0.06 0.07 0.08 0.09 0.1

2 How many hundredths is 0.07?
_____ hundredths

3 What is one-hundredth more than $\frac{8}{100}$ written as a decimal? _____

4 Which digit is missing from this sequence?
0.08, 0.09, 0.1, 0.11, 0.___2, 0.13

5 Mark 0.06 and 0.14 on this line.

0   0.1   0.2

6 Which is smaller: 0.1 or 0.01? _____

7 How many hundredths make one-tenth (or 0.1)?
_____ hundredths

8 What decimal is two-hundredths less than 0.1? _____

Now try these

9 True or false? 0.1 is the same as 0.10.   True ☐   False ☐

10 Which decimal (with two digits after the decimal point) lies between 0.14 and 0.16? _____

11 Circle the three decimals that lie between 0.1 and 0.2 in this list.

0.07   0.11   0.25   0.63   0.4   0.17   0.01   0.19

12 Write the two decimals marked with arrows. _____ and _____

0.2 ⬆   0.3   ⬆ 0.4

13 Luke says that 0.25 and 0.52 both lie between 0.2 and 0.3. Is he correct?

Yes ☐   No ☐

14 Which is larger: 0.29 or 0.31? _____

15 Circle the decimals that do not lie between 0.4 and 0.5 in this list.

0.4   0.5   0.6

0.53   0.41   0.74   0.45   0.63

16 Count back six-hundredths from 0.6. What decimal do you reach?

_____

Challenge

17 A centimetre is one-hundredth of a metre. How many centimetres is 0.58m? _____ cm

18 How many centimetres is: **a)** 0.8m? _____ cm   **b)** 0.08m? _____ cm

19 A television camera records an image every hundredth of a second. How many images are recorded in 0.7 seconds? _____

20 Write the missing decimals in this sequence.

0.85, _____ , 0.87, 0.88, 0.89, _____ , 0.91

21 How many hundredths is the difference between 0.9 and 0.81?

_____ hundredths

22 True or false? 0.60 is 54 hundredths greater than 0.6.   True ☐   False ☐

23 One year is one-hundredth of a century. What proportion of a century is 17 years? Give your answer as a decimal. _____

24 A dripping tap leaks 0.01 litres of water every minute. How many litres will it drip in 24 minutes?

_____ l

Key point

The digits after the decimal point are called **decimal places**.

Numbers like **0.54** and **1.27** are decimals with **two decimal places**.

	fraction	decimal ones . tenths hundredths
2 hundredths	$\frac{2}{100}$	0 . 0 2
14 hundredths	$\frac{14}{100}$	0 . 1 4
113 hundredths	$\frac{113}{100}$	1 . 1 3

Get started

1 What numbers are missing?

[ ] hundredths = 0.21

[ ] hundredths = 0.12

2 Circle which is more.

0.21   0.12

3 How many hundredths is 1.26?

_____ hundredths

4 How many hundredths more is 0.19 than 0.14? _____ hundredths

5 Which is greater: 0.75 or 0.57? _____

6 Which is the shorter length: 2.99cm or 3.01cm? _____ cm

7 Is 0.65kg more or less than 1kg?

_____

8 Which is more: £0.68 or £0.86?

£ _____

Now try these

9 True or false? 1.90 is greater than 0.95.   True [ ]   False [ ]

10 How many pence more is £1.01 than £0.99? _____ p

11 Use the < or > sign to show which is larger.   0.87 [ ] 0.93

12 Write a decimal with two decimal places that lies between 1.47 and 1.49. _____

36

13 True or false? 3.68 > 3.80   True ☐   False ☐

14 This shows part of a metre stick. The pencil is $\frac{14}{100}$ of a metre.

How would you write this as a decimal? _____ m

15 158 hundredths is the same as 1 one, 5 tenths and 8 hundredths.
How is this number written as a decimal? _____

16 A centimetre is one-hundredth of a metre. How do you write 75cm in metres? _____ m

Challenge

17 Put these decimals in order from smallest to largest.

0.64   0.85   0.69   _____ _____ _____

18 Josh and Mia are growing sunflowers. Josh's sunflower is 0.84m tall.
Mia's sunflower is 1.03m tall. Is Josh's sunflower taller or shorter
than Mia's? _____

19 Some athletes are doing the long jump. These are the lengths of their jumps:
James 3.10m   Kofi 2.87m   Dev 3.02m   Aiden 2.91m
Put their jumps in order from smallest to largest.

_____ m   _____ m   _____ m   _____ m

20 Freddie says that, because 7.5 and 7.50 are the same
number, then 7.5 is larger than 7.48. Is he correct?   Yes ☐   No ☐

21 Imogen has these four cards.
Use all the cards to make a decimal with two decimal places.
What is the:

| 1 | 4 | 7 | . |

a) smallest number that can be made? _____
b) largest number that can be made? _____

22 What is the smallest decimal with two decimal places that is greater than 3? _____

23 Rhys throws a shot-put 4.33m and Jason throws it 4.43m.
How much further does Jason throw than Rhys? _____ m

24 How much smaller than £33.57 is £33.42? Give your answer in pounds. £ _____

Key point

Any whole number can be easily divided by **100** using **place value** to give a decimal answer. To divide by 100, move the digits of the number **two places to the right**.

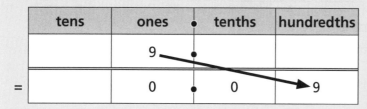

tens	ones	•	tenths	hundredths
	9			

÷ 100

=	tens	ones	•	tenths	hundredths
=		0	•	0	9

zero point zero nine

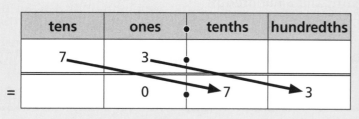

tens	ones	•	tenths	hundredths
7	3			

÷ 100

=	tens	ones	•	tenths	hundredths
=		0	•	7	3

zero point seven three

Get started

1 Divide the number in the grid by 100.

O	•	t	h
8	•		

_____

2 Divide the number in the grid by 100.

T	O	•	t	h
9	4	•		

_____

3 $6 ÷ 100 = \boxed{0.}$

4 Write the answer to $44 ÷ 100$ as a decimal. _____

5 What is 19 divided by 100 as a decimal? _____

6 $\boxed{} ÷ 100 = 0.26$

7 What is 45kg shared equally between 100 as a decimal? _____ kg

8 What number when divided by 100 gives 0.04? _____

Now try these

9 The arrow is pointing to the answer to the question $\boxed{} ÷ 100$.
What is the missing number in the question?

0.3 ↑ 0.4

10 100 people must equally pay for something costing £97.

How much should they each pay? £_____

11 Leo says that 5 ÷ 10 and 50 ÷ 100 have the same answer.

Is he correct?   Yes ☐   No ☐

12 Divide 8 by 100 and colour part of this whole square to show the answer.

13 If 69 ÷ 100 = 0.69, what is 0.69 × 100? _____

14 What is one-hundredth of 50 litres in litres and in millilitres?

_____ l or _____ ml

15 Lexie says 900 divided by 100 is 9.00 and Noor says 900 divided by 100 is 9.

Who is correct? Lexie, Noor or both? _____

16 Mark on the line the answer to 14 divided by 100.

```
0          0.1         0.2         0.3
```

Challenge

17 True or false? 100 lots of 0.13 is 13 wholes.   True ☐   False ☐

18 A 4m line is split into 100 equal parts. What is the length of each part:

a) in metres? _____ m   b) in centimetres? _____ cm   c) in millimetres? _____ mm

19 Divide 130 by 100. _____

20 A hose lets out 0.33 litres of water every second.
Lara's pond holds 33 litres.
How many seconds will it take to fill the pond? _____ sec

21 Hugh chooses a number to divide by 100. His answer as a mixed number is $7\frac{7}{100}$.

a) What is his answer as a decimal? _____

b) What was his chosen number? _____

22 A box containing 100 nails weighs 222 grams.
The box when empty weighs 12 grams. How much does each nail weigh? _____ g

23 What is one-hundredth of 30 plus one-tenth of 30? _____

24 Ella has £82. She spends one-hundredth of this money on some strawberries.

How much does she have left afterwards? £_____

Key point

To find a fraction of a quantity divide by the denominator (to find one part) and multiply by the numerator (to find several parts).

numerator ➙ $\dfrac{3}{10}$ of £50
denominator ➙

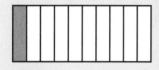

Divide the quantity by **10** to find **1 tenth**.
£50 ÷ 10 = £5

Then multiply the answer by **3** to find **3 tenths**.
£5 × 3 = £15, so $\dfrac{3}{10}$ of £50 = £15

Get started

1 Find $\dfrac{1}{5}$ of 35cm.

_____ cm

2 What is two-fifths of £35? £ _____

3 Find $\dfrac{7}{10}$ of 20kg. _____ kg

4 What length is two-fifths of this line?

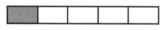

0   10cm _____ cm

5 Find $\dfrac{3}{4}$ of 40ml. _____ ml

6 Find $\dfrac{2}{7}$ of 35cm. _____ cm

7 Find two-thirds of 12p. _____ p

8 Find $\dfrac{7}{10}$ of 40g. _____ g

Now try these

9 A tenth of a kilogram of dog biscuits costs 15p.
What does two-tenths of a kilogram cost? _____ p

10 How many minutes in $\dfrac{3}{4}$ of an hour? _____ min

11 A full turn is 360°.
How many degrees in $\dfrac{2}{3}$ of a full turn? _____ °

12 True or false? $\dfrac{4}{9}$ of 27m = 12m

True ☐   False ☐

13 Fill in the missing number.

$\dfrac{}{6}$ of 12m = 10m

14 Ren takes three-quarters of the money in each box.
How much does he take in total? £ _____

15 How many minutes is $\dfrac{5}{6}$ of an hour?

_____ min

16 Four-sevenths of a class of 28 children wear glasses. How many children wear glasses? _____

Challenge

17 How much less than 64cm is $\dfrac{7}{8}$ of 64cm? _____ cm

18 A piece of ribbon is 54cm long. Sophie draws marks to divide it into nine equal parts.
With scissors, she cuts once so that she has two pieces of ribbon, one with 5 of the
parts and one with 4 of the parts. How long are the two pieces of ribbon?

_____ cm and _____ cm

19 Find the difference in kilograms between $\dfrac{3}{5}$ of 45kg and $\dfrac{5}{6}$ of 36kg. _____ kg

20

| $\dfrac{2}{3}$ of £36 | $\dfrac{5}{8}$ of £40 | $\dfrac{7}{10}$ of £30 |

Look at the fractions above. What is the value of: **a)** the largest of these amounts? £_____

b) the smallest of these amounts? £_____

21 Curtis is $\dfrac{7}{9}$ the height of his brother. His brother is 108cm tall.

a) How tall is Curtis? _____ cm

b) How many centimetres taller than Curtis is his brother? _____ cm

22 One-twelfth of an hour is 5 minutes.
What fraction of an hour is 55 minutes? _____ hr

23 The length of a rectangle is 16cm. Its width is three-eighths of its length.
Find the perimeter of the rectangle. _____ cm

24 Seventeen-hundredths = $\dfrac{17}{100}$ = 0.17. What is seventeen-hundredths of £200? £_____

Key point

Fractions can be used to show parts of a whole unit of measurement or money such as a kilogram, a metre, a litre, an hour or a pound.

Fractions with tenths and hundredths can also be shown as decimals.

$5\frac{7}{10}$ cm = 5.7cm $\frac{13}{100}$ kg = 0.13kg $9\frac{8}{100}$ ml = 9.08ml

Get started

1 How many minutes is $\frac{1}{2}$ an hour?

_____ min

2 Write $3\frac{7}{10}$ m as a decimal. _____ m

3 How many hundredths of a pound is £0.64?

_____ hundredths

4 How many quarters of a kilogram are in $2\frac{1}{4}$ kilograms?

_____ quarters

5 True or false? $3\frac{1}{100}$ kg = 3.1kg

True ☐   False ☐

6 Find three-fifths of 50cm. _____ cm

0 ├───┼───┼───┼───┼───┤ 50cm

7 How many minutes is one-tenth of an hour? _____ min

8 What is one-third of 75ml? _____ ml

Now try these

9 | 100cm = 1m |

Use this fact to write 1cm as:

a) a fraction of a metre. _____ m   **b)** a decimal. _____ m

10 Mark a cross on the ruler to show 2.7cm.

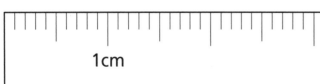

1cm

11 Circle the parcel with the heaviest mass.

 $4\frac{3}{10}$ kg

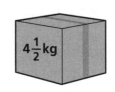 $4\frac{1}{2}$ kg

 4.7kg

12 A 1m plank of wood is cut into 10 equal lengths.
What fraction of a metre are 7 of these lengths together? _____ m

13 A garden statue is $4\frac{9}{10}$m high. The hedge beside it is $5\frac{6}{10}$m high.

How much taller is the hedge than the statue? Give your answer as a decimal. _____ m

14 Sana has twenty 5p coins, making a total of £1. What fraction of one pound is:

a) 5p? _____   b) 95p? _____

15 Find the difference in grams between $\frac{3}{4}$ of 32g and $\frac{7}{8}$ of 24g. _____ g

16 True or false? 60 lots of $\frac{1}{100}$kg = $\frac{60}{100}$kg = $\frac{6}{10}$kg = 0.6kg   True ☐   False ☐

Challenge

17 What is three-eighths of a litre less than 7 litres? _____ l

18 Leah puts 0.7kg of pasta into an empty bowl.
She puts the bowl and pasta on some weighing scales. The total mass is 1.2kg.
How much more does the pasta weigh than the empty bowl? _____ kg

19 As she walks, each of Beth's steps is $\frac{2}{5}$m apart.
If she takes 3 steps, how far from the start has she walked?

_____ m

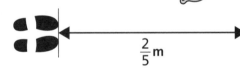

$\frac{2}{5}$m

20 Some athletes are doing the long jump.   Kate 5.1m   Abby 3.5m   Jess 4.2m   Amna 4.5m

Who jumps 4 metres when rounded to the nearest whole metre? _____

21 Pippa spent three-tenths of her birthday
money on a coat. If she is left with £70,
how much was her birthday money in total? £_____

22 Some square tiles have sides that are each $\frac{55}{100}$ of a metre.

How long is a line of 3 touching tiles, in metres?

Give your answer as a decimal. _____ m

23 Evan ran a race in $10\frac{2}{5}$ seconds. Will ran it in $10\frac{4}{10}$ seconds.

What is the difference in seconds between the two times? _____ sec

24 A machine makes 100 rings from a piece of metal weighing 80g.
What is the weight of each ring as a decimal if no metal is wasted? _____ g

Check-up test 3

1 Write the decimal 0.03 as a fraction. _____

1 mark

2 Colour 39 hundredths of this whole.

1 mark

3 What decimal has no ones, 3 tenths and 4 hundredths? _____

1 mark

4 A class of 30 pupils get into 5 equal groups with 6 children in each group.
Write as a decimal what proportion of the class are 12 of the children. _____

1 mark

5 Mark 0.09 and 0.12 on this line.

0   0.1   0.2

1 mark

6 Circle the three decimals that lie between 0.3 and 0.4.

0.47   0.41   0.35   0.61   0.4   0.37   0.31   0.29

1 mark

7 A centimetre is one-hundredth of a metre.
How many centimetres is 0.74m? _____ cm

1 mark

8 Circle which is more.

0.34   0.43

1 mark

9 Use the < or > sign to show which is larger.

0.53 [ ] 0.71

1 mark

10 Bailey and Domino are two donkeys at the stable.
Bailey is 1.19m tall. Domino is 0.95m tall.
Is Bailey taller or shorter than Domino? _____

1 mark

11 Write the answer to 37 ÷ 100 as a decimal. _____

1 mark

12 Mark on the line the answer to 26 divided by 100.

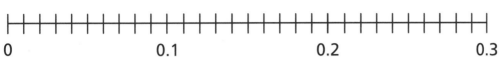

0   0.1   0.2   0.3

1 mark

13 Divide 170 by 100. _____

1 mark

14 Find $\frac{3}{10}$ of 30kg. _____ kg

1 mark

15 A tenth of a kilogram of bird food costs 25p.
What does three-tenths of a kilogram cost?

_____ p

1 mark

16 Find the difference in kilograms between $\frac{5}{8}$ of 32kg and $\frac{3}{5}$ of 30kg. _____ kg

1 mark

17 One-twelfth of an hour is 5 minutes.
What fraction of an hour is 35 minutes? _____ hr

1 mark

18 How many quarters of a kilogram are in $1\frac{3}{4}$ kilograms? _____ quarters

1 mark

19 Mark a cross on the ruler to show 2.4cm.

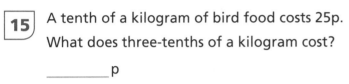

1cm

1 mark

20 Some athletes are throwing the javelin.
Their throws are:
Ben 25.3m   Ava 24.5m   Ellen 25.6m   Kai 24.3m

Which athletes' throws are 25 metres when
rounded to the nearest whole metre?

_____

1 mark

Total

20 marks

Final test

Section 1

1 $\dfrac{2}{\boxed{}}$ is equivalent to $\dfrac{6}{\boxed{}}$.

1 mark

2 For each diagram write the fraction of the shape that is red.

a)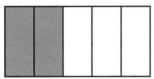

b)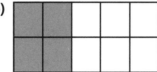

c)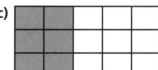

_____   _____   _____

1 mark

3 Circle any fractions that are equivalent to one-quarter.

$\dfrac{2}{6}$ $\dfrac{2}{8}$ $\dfrac{5}{12}$ $\dfrac{3}{9}$ $\dfrac{3}{12}$ $\dfrac{5}{20}$

1 mark

Section 2

4 How many hundredths is the same as one-tenth? _____ hundredths

1 mark

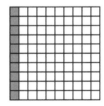

5 Write the answer to 1 ÷ 100 as a fraction. _____

1 mark

6 Continue this sequence. $\dfrac{8}{100}$, $\dfrac{9}{100}$, $\dfrac{1}{10}$, $\dfrac{11}{100}$, _____ , _____

1 mark

Section 3

7 Find $\dfrac{3}{4}$ of £100. £_____

1 mark

8 Find $\dfrac{3}{7}$ of 35cm. _____ cm

1 mark

9 A toy piano is 108cm tall. The stool is $\dfrac{5}{9}$ the height of the piano.

How tall is the stool? _____ cm

1 mark

46

Section 4

10 What is five-sevenths more than three-sevenths as a mixed number? _____

1 mark

11 $\dfrac{3}{8} + \dfrac{5}{8} + \dfrac{5}{8} = \dfrac{\boxed{}}{\boxed{}}$

1 mark

12 $\dfrac{11}{12} - \dfrac{4}{12} = \dfrac{\boxed{}}{\boxed{}}$

1 mark

Section 5

13 Write all these fractions as decimals.

$$\dfrac{1}{10} \quad \dfrac{11}{100} \quad \dfrac{13}{10} \quad \dfrac{6}{100} \quad \dfrac{142}{100}$$

_____ _____ _____ _____ _____

1 mark

14 True or false? $\dfrac{73}{100}$ = 73 hundredths = 7 tenths + 3 hundredths = 7.3

True ☐   False ☐

1 mark

15 Write the decimal that is 2 ones and 3 hundredths. _____

1 mark

Section 6

16 What is one-half written as a decimal?

$\dfrac{1}{2} = \dfrac{?}{10} = \boxed{}$

1 mark

17 $\dfrac{1}{4}$ of this square is red. $\dfrac{3}{4}$ of this square is white.

Write $\dfrac{1}{4}$ as a decimal. _____

1 mark

18 Write $\dfrac{3}{4}$ as a decimal. _____

1 mark

please turn over

47

Final test

Section 7

19 Answer these four questions, giving each answer as a fraction or mixed number.

$7 \div 10 = \dfrac{}{}$ $19 \div 10 = \dfrac{}{}$ $9 \div 100 = \dfrac{}{}$ $49 \div 100 = \dfrac{}{}$

☐ 1 mark

20 Answer the same four questions, giving each answer as a decimal.

$7 \div 10 = \boxed{}$ $19 \div 10 = \boxed{}$ $9 \div 100 = \boxed{}$ $49 \div 100 = \boxed{}$

☐ 1 mark

21 Circle the decimal that shows three-tenths and one-hundredth.

1.3   3.1   0.13   0.31   3.01

☐ 1 mark

Section 8

22 Round each decimal to the nearest whole number.

0.6 → _____   3.8 → _____   7.4 → _____   9.5 → _____   0.2 → _____

☐ 1 mark

23 Circle the decimal which, when rounded to the nearest whole number, rounds to 8.

8.8   0.8   3.8   6.5   8.5   7.7   9.1

☐ 1 mark

24 Write the missing digit to show the smallest decimal
with one place that rounds to the nearest whole number 5. $\boxed{4.}$

☐ 1 mark

Section 9

25 Use either the < or > sign to show which is larger.

0.8 ☐ 0.6   5.3 ☐ 7.1

☐ 1 mark

26 Circle the larger decimal.   0.73   0.69

☐ 1 mark

27 Write these decimals from smallest to largest.

0.75   1.03   0.94   _____ _____ _____

☐ 1 mark

48

Section 10

28 Iona has £69. She spends one-hundredth of this money.
How much does she have left afterwards?

£_____

1 mark

29 Kasper is 0.89m tall. His brother is 1.01m tall.
Is his brother taller or shorter than Kasper?

_____

1 mark

30 Mariam puts 0.9kg of flour into an empty bowl.
She puts the bowl and flour on some weighing scales.
The total mass is $1\frac{1}{10}$kg.
How much does the empty bowl weigh?
Write your answer as a decimal.

_____ kg

1 mark

Total

30 marks

End of test

49

How did I find it?

Unit		Difficult	Getting there	Easy
1	I can understand the role of the numerator and denominator.			
2	I can use fractions in different representations, including sets.			
3	I can use mixed numbers.			
4	I can find equivalent fractions using a fraction wall.			
5	I can use patterns within families of equivalent fractions.			
6	I can add and subtract fractions with the same denominator.			
	Check-up test 1			
7	I can use tenths as fractions and decimals.			
8	I can find decimals with one decimal place on a number line.			
9	I can order and round decimals with one decimal place.			
10	I can divide one-digit numbers by 10.			
11	I can divide one- or two-digit numbers by 10.			
12	I can understand fractions and decimals as the result of division.			
	Check-up test 2			
13	I can recognise hundredths as fractions and decimals.			
14	I can find decimals with two decimal places on a number line.			
15	I can compare and order decimals with two decimal places.			
16	I can divide one- or two-digit numbers by 100.			
17	I can solve problems, including finding fractions of amounts.			
18	I can solve problems with money and measures.			
	Check-up test 3			
	Final test			